CW00384232

Jazz classics

For SSA Choir With Piano Accompaniment

Arranged by Berty Rice

Music set by Andrew Shiels
Cover design by Miranda Harvey
Printed in the United Kingdom

Novello Publishing Limited
8-9 Frith Street London W1D 3JB

When Sunny Gets Blue

Words by Jack Segal
Music by Marvin Fisher

That's how she got her name. Since that sad af- fair, she's

That's how she got her name. Since that sad af- fair, she's

That's how she got her name. Since that sad af- fair, she's

Em⁷ Gmaj⁷/A C⁹/G F♯m⁷ B⁷ B♭(add⁹) F⁶/A F/G

lost her smile, changed her style. Some-how she's not the same.

lost her smile, changed her style. Some-how she's not the same. But

lost her smile, changed her style. Some-how she's not the same.

Cmaj⁷ Am⁷ Fmaj⁷ Dm⁹ D♭⁹ Gm⁷/C B♭maj⁷/C Caug

8

hold her near when Sun-ny gets blue.

hold her near when Sun-ny gets blue.

hold her near when Sun-ny gets blue.

Fever

Words & Music by John Davenport & Eddie Cooley

Sun lights up the day - time,
Sun lights up the day - time,
Sun lights up the day - time,

F7(♯9)   B♭m7 N.C.

moon lights up the night.__ I light up__ when you call__
moon lights up the night.__ I light up__ when you call__
moon lights up the night.__ I light up__ when you call__

that is some-thing you all know.___ Fe-ver is-n't

that is some-thing you all know.___ Fe-ver is-n't

that is some-thing you all know.___ Fe-ver is-n't

such a new___ thing, fe-ver start-ed long___ a - go:___

such a new___ thing, fe-ver start-ed long a - go:___

such a new___ thing, fe-ver start-ed long a - go:___

Ro - me - o loved Ju - liet, Ju - li - et she felt__ the same.__

When he put his arms a - round__ her, he said, "Oh

leggiero

Soprano 1

Fe - ver,__

Soprano 2

Fe - ver,

Alto

Ju - lie, ba - by you're__ my flame.__ Thou gi - vest fe - ver

87

sub p

_ They give you fe - ver   when you kiss them,   fe -ver if you live_ and learn._

_ They give you fe - ver   when you kiss them,   fe -ver if you live_ and learn._

_ They give you fe - ver   when you kiss them,   fe -ver if you live_ and learn._

Am⁷   N.C.

ppp

p

91

Fe - ver   till you siz - zle.

Fe - ver   till you siz - zle.

Fe - ver   till you siz - zle.

Lullaby of Birdland

Words by George David Weiss
Music by George Shearing

Soprano 1: could there be ways— to re-veal— in a phrase— how I feel!—

Soprano 2:

Alto:

Cm7　F7(♭9)　B♭maj7　E♭7　A7(♭5)　D7

Have you e-ver heard two— tur-tle doves— bill and coo—

Have you e-ver heard two— tur-tle doves— bill and coo—

Gm　Gm/E　A7　D7　Gm　E♭maj7

high in the sky— up a - bove,— all be - cause— we're in love!

high in the sky up a - bove,— all be - cause— we're in love!

high in the sky— up a - bove,— all be - cause— we're in love!

Cm⁷   F⁷⁽♭⁹⁾   Fm/D   G⁷   Cm⁷   F⁷   B♭⁶

Same tempo, not swung, 16ths feel

Cm⁷   E♭/D♭   D⁷⁽♭¹³⁾   Gm   Adim⁷   Gm/B♭   G/B   Cm⁷   E♭/D♭   D⁷⁽♭¹³⁾

mf

Soprano 1   *mf*

Lul - la - by of Bird - land,

Gm   Adim⁷   B♭⁶   Bdim⁷   Cm⁷   E♭/D♭   D⁷sus⁴   D⁷   Gm   Adim⁷   B♭maj⁷   G⁷/B

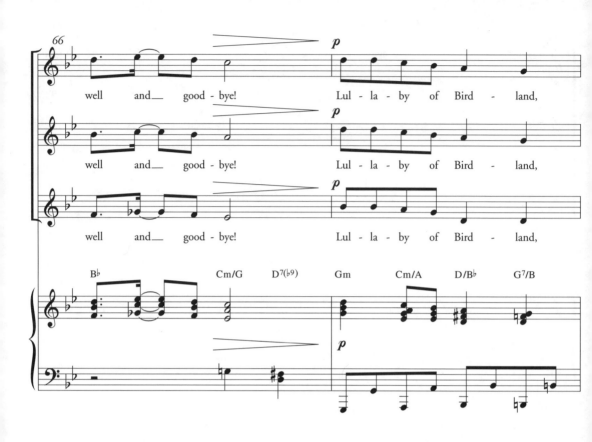

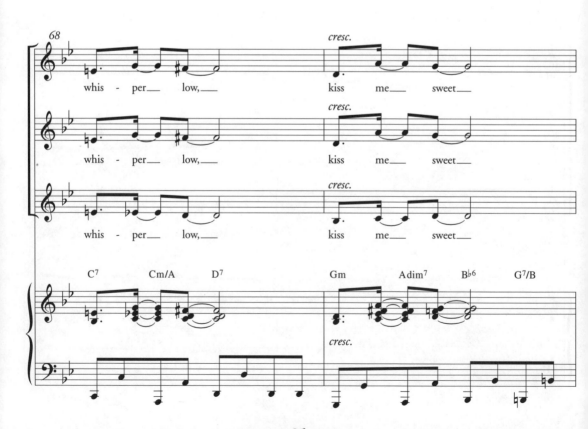

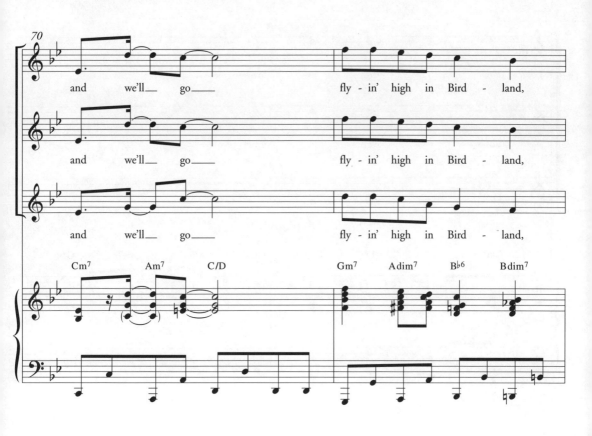

37

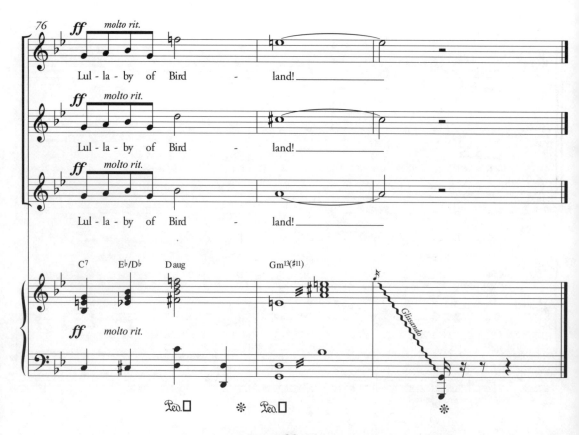

Fly Me To The Moon

Words & Music by Bart Howard

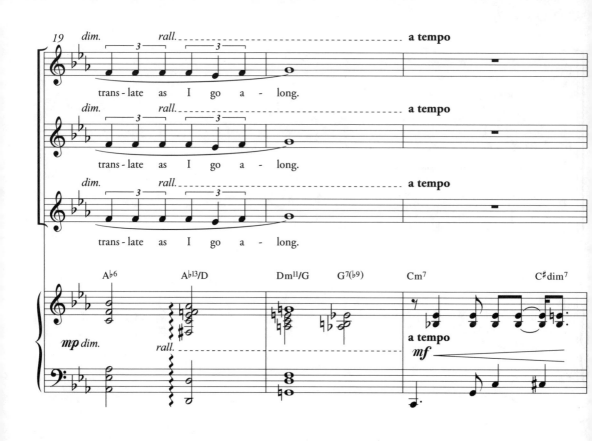

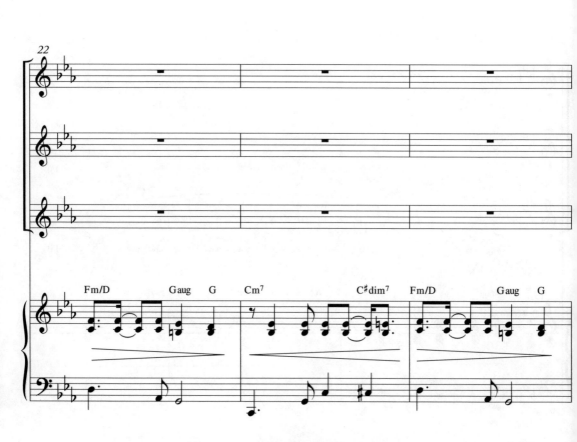

Ju - pi - ter and Mars.___ In o - ther words:___

Ju - pi - ter and Mars.___

Ju - pi - ter and Mars.___

G7   Cm7   Fm

senza ped.

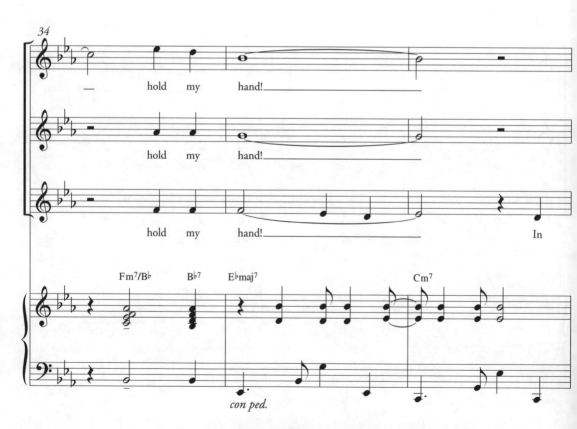

___ hold my hand!_____

hold my hand!_____

hold my hand!_____ In

Fm7/Bb   Bb7   Ebmaj7   Cm7

con ped.

sing   for   e - ver - more;___   You   are   all   I   long_

sing   for   e - ver - more;___   You   are   all   I   long_

sing   for   e - ver - more;___   You   are   all   I   long_

B♭   E♭maj⁷   A♭

___ for,___   all   I   wor - ship and   a - dore.___   In

___ for,___   all   I   wor - ship and   a - dore.___

___ for,___   all   I   wor - ship and   a - dore.___

Fm/D   G⁷   Cm⁷   C⁷⁽♭⁹⁾

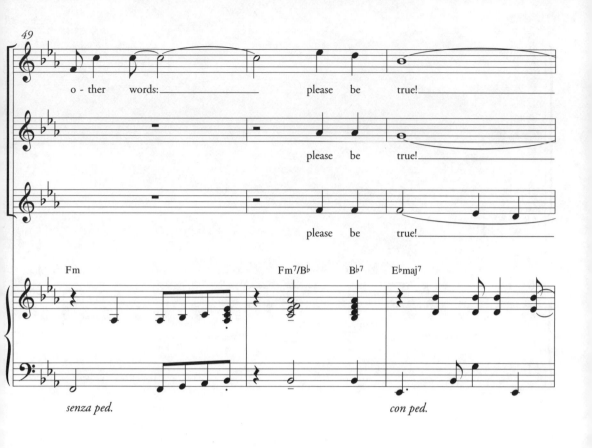

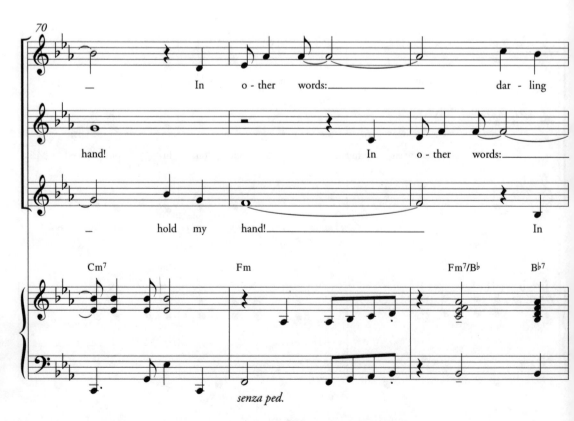

51

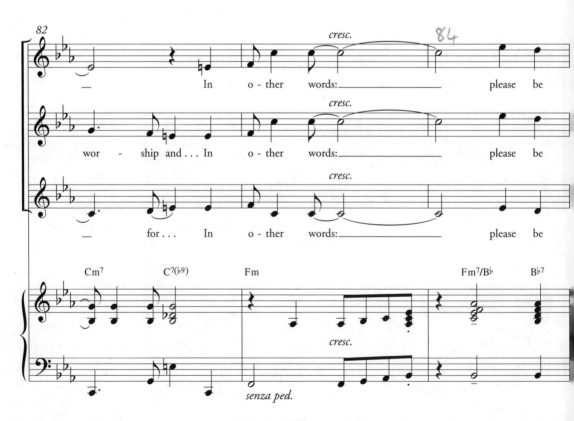

53

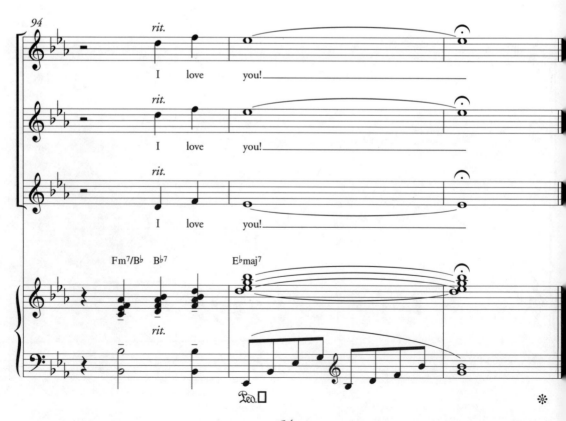

Misty

Words by Johnny Burke
Music by Erroll Garner

help-less as a kit-ten up a tree, and I feel like I'm cling-ing to a cloud. I

help-less as a kit-ten up a tree, and I feel like I'm cling-ing to a cloud. I

help-less as a kit-ten up a tree, and I feel like I'm cling-ing to a cloud. I

can't____ un-der - stand,____ I get mis - ty just hold - ing your hand.____

can't____ un-der - stand,____ I get mis - ty just hold - ing your hand.____

can't____ un-der - stand,____ I get mis - ty just hold - ing your hand.____

mu - sic I hear;___ I get mis - ty the mo - ment you're near.

mu - sic I hear;___ I get mis - ty the mo - ment you're near.

mu - sic I hear;___ I get mis - ty the mo - ment you're near.

Bm⁷   Em⁷   Am⁷   D⁷   Gmaj⁷   Cm/G

You're lead-ing me on,___

You're lead-ing me on,___

You can say that you're lead - ing me on,___ but it's just what I

G   Dm⁹   Dm   Ddim⁷/G

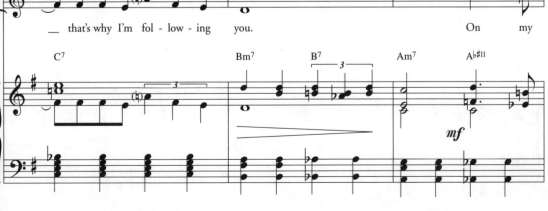

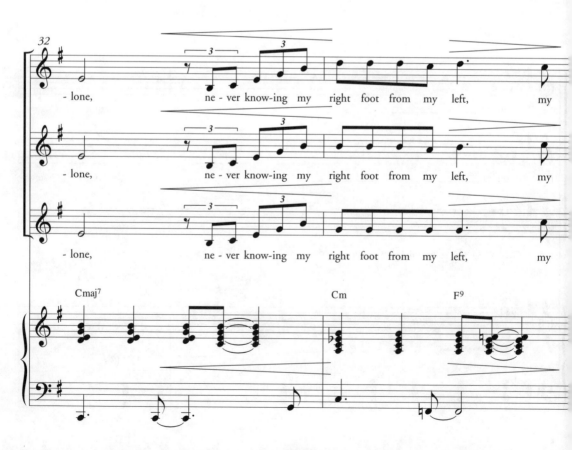

On my own,   would I   wan - der through this won-der - land a -

On my own,   would I   wan - der through this won-der - land a -

On my own,   would I   wan - der through this won-der - land a -

9/02 (45412)